Dear ANORAK friends,

As you loyal readers will agree, every issue of ANORAK is special. Well, this one is 23 gazillion times more special than the previous one or even future ones. The reason is that it marks our 10th anniversary.

WE ARE 10 YEARS OLD!

Ten years ago, we launched our very first issue of ANORAK, because we were looking for a fun magazine that would feed our brains and help us be even more creative. We also wanted an opportunity to share some of our favourite worst jokes.

Ten years later, we have all grown up a little, but not much really. We still like terrible puns, silly stories and are more passionate than ever about having fun, learning and letting our imaginations run wild.

This brilliant journey wouldn't have been possible without you lovely people who have been buying, contributing to and supporting our Happy Mag for Kids for all this time. For that, here's my message to you:

Thank you! Thank you! Thank you! Thank you! Thank you!

From the bottom of my heart.

It's always a lot of fun producing ANORAK and I hope it will continue to inspire you to draw, imagine and be silly too.

Enjoy this PARTY special edition and may I please reiterate this very important message I have for you:

Thank you! Thank you! Thank you! Thank you! Thank you!

Thank you! Thank you! Thank you!

Cathy

The Jump

Story by Jack Goddard

When I turned 10 years old, I was brave enough to jump.

As a child, I spent a lot of time at my Nanny's house, out in the country.
My brother Conor and I had many adventures in the woods with my Nanny's dog, Tushka.
She was an easily scared dog and jumped at any noise.

On one cold Autumn morning, we took Tushka out.
The fields and woods were thick with mud, and the puddles as deep as rivers.
As I skipped along by Conor's side,
we suddenly heard birds flying out of the trees. I looked up,
while frightened Tushka ran off, and next thing I knew...

SPLOSH!

...Tushka had propelled me into the biggest
muddy puddle in the field! Conor pulled me
out of the mud that covered me like a blanket.
Tushka had run along but we soon caught up
with her before she could go too far away.
We were relieved to have her back,
and as I stood there, I noticed something...

My left wellie had disappeared into the mud!

We went back every day to look for my boot.
We searched the field all over,
but we could never find it. Nanny never managed to either,
nor could Tushka. It must have been sucked straight into the mud
and gone deep underground.

That night I had a dream that my wellie had turned into a seed.
As the days went by, it slowly grew,
until it was the biggest tree in the field!
During Spring it blossomed with leftie wellies.
In my dream, Nanny and me stopped for a while
to admire our tree.

Maybe if I go back there now, I may find the Wellie Tree...

I wish I could go back.

Illustrations by
Ruby Hinton

Rest in Peace Nanny

The Weather Shop

"ALWAYS TAKE THE WEATHER WITH YOU"

we are OPEN

POST

WELCOME

Illustrations by Jayde Perkin

Don't forget we have discount on hailstones today.
Two jars for the price of one!

What is
your bestseller
for the month?

At this time
of the year,
sunshine and
showers are
very popular.
But it's a bit
predictable. Can
I interest you in
some snow?

My cat won't
like snow.

Maybe I will
go for fog.

Fog is always
a winner
and always
magical.

Yes!
It means
we can
play hide
and seek
all day!

Excuse me, how much is lighting please?

It's twenty bobs
for ten strikes.

Perfect. I will have two then please.
It's my son's graduation day and
it'll be fun to add
a bit of drama to the
proceedings!

THE WIND

BY OLIVE GORMLEY (NINE YEARS OLD)

If you went past the Old Beaver and the Fluffy Duck, you would find the Tree Trunk.
Down the Tree Trunk you would find a tunnel with walls covered in pictures of snooty Kings and Queens
and green ivy falling down from the ceilings. Down, down you would go until you reach the market of
the River Weavers. There, food is being handed out from the stalls, the most mouth-watering food you
will ever taste. A small door suddenly opened between two stalls and out came a River Weaver.
She wore a grass woven dress and her name was Rut.
She walked around the market, inhaling all the beautiful smells from the food stalls.

There she met another River Weaver, Nix.
Together they decided to explore outside. They pressed their tiny hands on a crusty bark door.
"Creak!" went the door and, "Good luck" it added. They jumped into the river and started to swim upwards.
They stopped in their tracks when they saw fish blood trickling down. Hunting season had obviously started.
Shivering, they walked back to the warm tunnel, which was very welcoming after the cold of the water.

Rut turned to Nix *"I can't do this."* She shook her head in disbelief, recalling the fish's pleading eyes.
"I have to leave." Nix's face grew pale. *"You can't! You know the terrible things they do to pixies who leave."*
But it was plain to see Rut was not going to give up.

The morning after, Rut got up early and, grabbing her backpack, she silently crept out of her room.
She saw Nix's face squashed against a window, and waved her goodbye.
She turned around and tripped, which woke up the guards. Rut could only think of one thing to do: run.
She ran and ran more. She pushed the oak door and jumped into the river. She swam to the top of the river and then ran some
more. She looked up and found the sky not blue with pearly white clouds but grey with angry ones instead.
A fierce wind started and whipped her bag off her back.
Throat tightening she croaked, *"No! Not my food, my clothes, my money!"*

The ominously whistling wind and terrifying lightning gave her the chase.
She noticed a tunnel, jumped in it, shut her eyes and waited for the wind to cease.

She woke up with a warm light shining on her face. The storm had stopped and had been replaced by
the faint whispering of the breeze. She got to her feet and continued her journey.
On the floor, she found a bronze coin.
She looked into it and made a wish. She heard footsteps echoing from wall to wall.
She turned around and saw a medium sized hairy creature looking at her with bright keen eyes, tongue lolling.
Rut had never seen these before. *"A dog?"* she wondered.
She tentatively stretched her hand towards it and the dog leapt up.
She then saw a boy with a cheeky grin.
"Hello, I'm Charlie." He gestured towards the dog.
"This is Henry. I'm presuming you are a River Weaver?"
"Yes I am. Are you a Water Spinner?"
"Kind of. I left the lake a few days ago to study plants and animals. I want to be a doctor you see."
Henry barked. *"Do you want to find a better place to live as well?"* Rut asked.
Charlie nodded.
"Friends?" Rut asked.
Charlie grinned.

Rut showed Charlie her bronze coin and they soon realised what it was for. It was a Looking Desire.
You look into the bronze, see your reflection and it will show you the way.
It showed Rut where to find Charlie and showed Charlie where edible berries were.
Soon they came to an open clearing. The grass was thick and lush. Henry leapt around and played with bunnies.
They decided this was a perfect place to make a burrow.
They started digging and Rut thought, "*The wind took my bag but gave me a present: new friends.*"

So, if you ever go to the River Weavers' burrows you're going to have to look a bit further to find Rut and Charlie.
And maybe, just maybe, you might get some help from the wind. It is very possible.

Words by Olive Gormley (9 years old), illustrations by Noa Snir

ROUND BUNNY

CREATED BY GASTON CABA

Fold this bit here to bring Round B. and his friend Round G. together.

Fold this bit here to bring Round B. and his friend Round G. together.

HARVEY'S BIRTHDAY

Words by Roy Edwards, illustrations by Letizia Iannaccone

Harvey the harvest mouse woke one day,
"I'm eleventy seven hooray!
It's the Wunth of Octember
And well, if I remember
My birthday's that very day."

So the word went out to the fields and the woods
To the valleys, the hills and the dales.
"Harvey's party will be
At a quarter to three,
All are welcome, so don't drag your tails".

The cat, the rat and the pippistrelle bat
All arrived with gifts of grain.
The hoverfly dithered,
The slow worm slithered
All thought it might come on to rain.

The hare and the tortoise arrived quite late,
They had only just finished their race.
The hare was distraught, as
He'd lost to the tortoise
And had only achieved second place.

Said the bumble bee,
"Who invited that flea?
It tickles and makes me scratch".
"Not me," said the hen,
"I must leave now and then,
To sit on my eggs till they hatch".

At the end of the day
Harvey said, "Now let's play
On our flutes, violins and tin whistles."
So they did that all night
In the pale moonlight
As they sat on their toadstools and thistles.

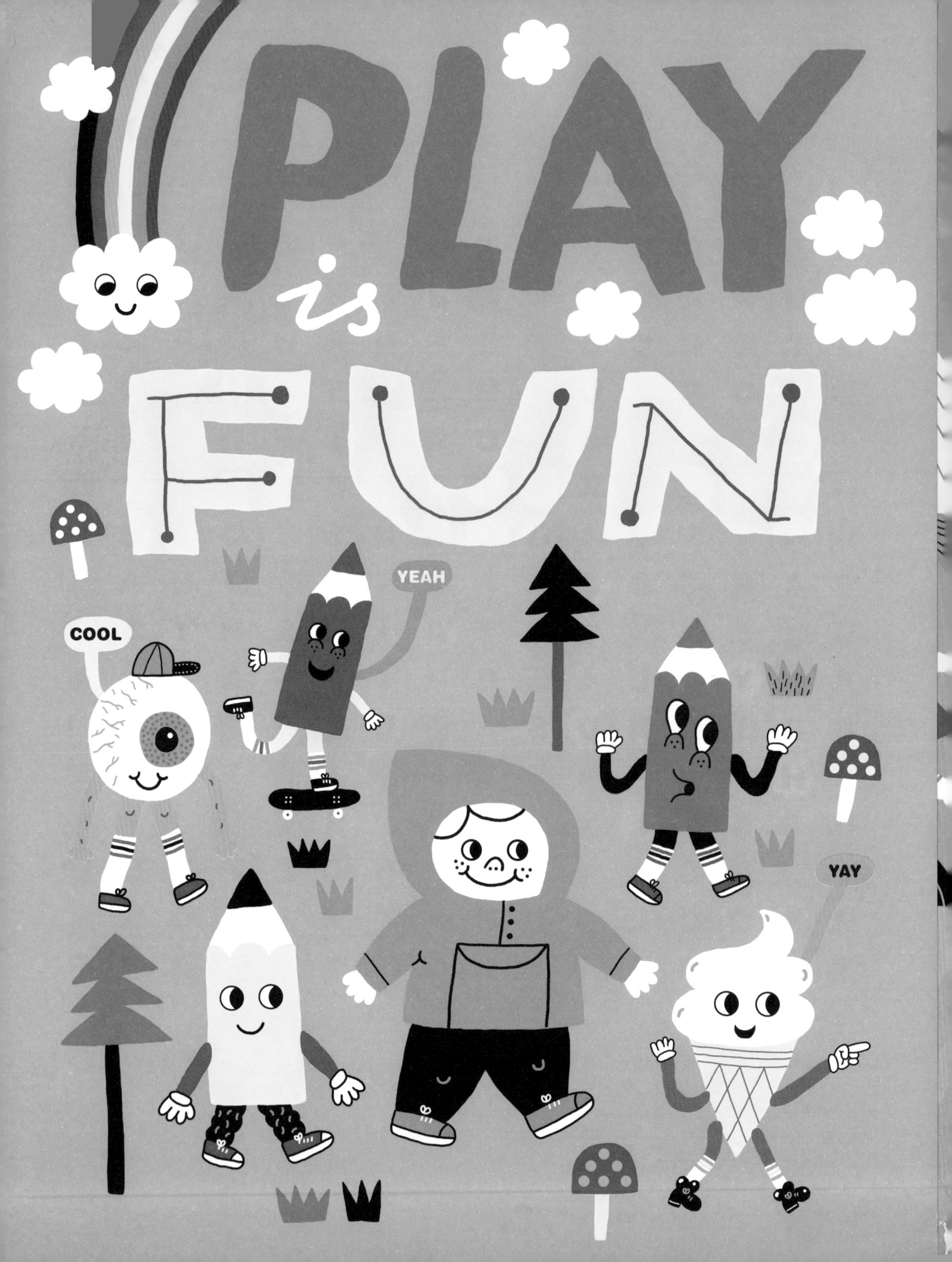
PLAY
is
FUN
YEAH
COOL
YAY

Illustrations by Idiot's Pasture

PING PONG PAUL

There was once a chap
who lived somewhere off the map.
His name was Paul,
but he wasn't a Gaul.

What he liked to do all day
was work, work and play.
Not any games, mind.
Just the table tennis kind.

For Ping Pong was his name
and Ping Pong was his game.
He played from morning to night.
Played, played, he played a lot alright.

He was once invited to show off his skills
in a mighty event, in the city of Vilz.
He had to play against his arch enemy,
The longest match ever recorded in history.

For that he trained night, day and a bit more,
determined to beat Ping Pong Laure.
It took ages, they couldn't find a winner.
Bored, the sleepy crowd left for dinner.

As it came close to the 24th hour
Paul hit a shot full of power.
Exhausted, Laure missed the ball.
This meant Paul was the winner after all.

Words by Oscar Olmedillas Benady

The Heroes of my Mind

Illustrated by Robbie Cathro.

EVERY NIGHT I THINK ABOUT THE HEROES I SEE ON TV. THE ONES I READ IN MY COMICS. AND THOSE THAT EXIST IN MY MIND. THEY DESCEND FROM A GOLDEN NIGHT SKY ON A MARSHMALLOW RING STRAIGHT FROM THE STARS. THEY LAND SOFTLY IN MY DREAMS AND TOGETHER WE GO ON EXCITING ADVENTURES THAT STOP ME FROM WAKING UP. THEY ARE SOOT SPRITES. MAGICAL STONES. SONGS OF GOLD AND ALL THESE TOO...

Happy Birthday

It's our birthday, hooray!
Here, we explore weird and wonderful
birthday traditions around the world.

Who has seen the most birthdays ever? We have seen 10. Not bad.
But not as good as Mbah Gotho, who has seen 145 birthdays. 145!
This means he was born in the 19th Century, two centuries ago!
He was born before some of the things we take for granted like cars,
phones, cinema, aeroplanes and television were invented!
Imagine what you would do if you lived that long?

For a long time, not everyone celebrated their birthdays.
Most people didn't even know what date they were
born in as it was never recorded. Birthday parties
were reserved for Kings and Gods. The Romans
came along and decided that everyone
deserved a birthday. That's great, huh?
Except it wasn't quite everyone.
Boys deserved to have a birthday
celebration, but girls? Nope.
Not a Roman chance.
How unfair is that?

JANUS

It is our ancestors the Greeks we need to thank for birthday cakes. When worshipping the Goddess of the Moon, Artemis, they made a round cake (like the moon) with candles to reflect the light (of the moon). But it is the Germans in the 1700s who made it a fun thing to have for ALL birthday parties. Danke German people!

If one birthday isn't enough for you, why not have two? Kings and Queens have two, one public and one private. As you are the Kings and Queens of Anorak Land, we'd be quite happy if you had two, provided you invite us to both! If you reach the grand old age of 100 years old, the Queen will send you a birthday card. That means we have only 90 years to wait for ours. SIGH.

Instead of two, how about just one birthday for everyone? That's what people in Vietnam do: they celebrate their birthdays altogether, with the entire nation. During the Tet festival, everyone parties for a day or even a week welcoming the New Near and everyone's new year. That's one way of saving on birthday cards!

Chúc mừng sinh nhật!

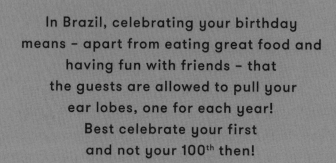

OUCH!

In Brazil, celebrating your birthday
means – apart from eating great food and
having fun with friends – that
the guests are allowed to pull your
ear lobes, one for each year!
Best celebrate your first
and not your 100ᵗʰ then!

If you live in Australia, a birthday party
is not complete without Fairy Bread.
Sorry to disappoint but
it is not a cake made by actual
fairies. It is white bread
sprinkled with butter
and covered with
multi coloured sprinkles.
Yumbo!

Some birthday celebrations sound a bit dangerous to us!
If you live in the island of Vanuatu (South Pacific),
the way to celebrate your coming of age is to jump off
a terrifying 98-foot tall tower with a vine
tied to your ankles! Sounds scary
but so much fun too!

The most famous of all birthdays has to be
Christmas Day. It marks Jesus' birthday.
However, it is not actually the day he was born.
No-one really knows when Jesus was born
but the Romans decided it had to be nine months
after the first day of Spring which
falls on March 25ᵗʰ. Nine months
after makes 25ᵗʰ December. Ta-da!

If you were born on Christmas Day,
otherwise known as not-Jesus-birthday day,
you are officially the most precious
of all creatures. That's because Christmas birthdays
are the rarest of them all! Do you know the question
most frequently asked if you are born on Christmas day?
Do you get two presents?
The answer is YES.
You do.*

If you celebrate your birthday in China, you will very likely
be offered the 'longevity noodles'. These yummy noodles
are made from one long strand of noodle
which you need to eat without breaking it.
This will bring you a very long life...
and the world's record for the longest
slurping contest ever!

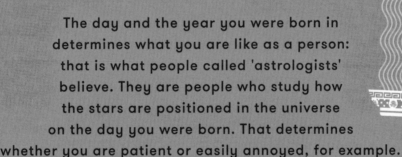

The day and the year you were born in
determines what you are like as a person:
that is what people called 'astrologists'
believe. They are people who study how
the stars are positioned in the universe
on the day you were born. That determines
whether you are patient or easily annoyed, for example.
They also claim to be able to predict personal events.
That's what you can read in a horoscope,
which you can find in newspapers and magazines.
For a very special ANORAK horoscope, turn to the last
pages of our happy mag!

FALLING
OBJECTS

BEWARE OF
SHARKS

3

2

1

*Disclaimer: Anorak's editor was born on Christmas Day. Please send double the presents at the address shown at the back of the magazine.

Time to Party

Held every January and now in its 38th year, the Straw Bear Festival is one where local men make and wear giant costumes made of straw to celebrate the start of the agricultural year. They parade around town all throughout the first day, and on the final day they get burnt.
Just the costumes, not the people inside!

The good people of India and Nepal have the most joyful way we know of to celebrate the new season: they throw powders of bright colours at each other! Called the Holi festival, it is spent dancing, visiting friends, eating delicious food and getting covered in green, pink, yellow and orange powder. Best party ever!

One festival in Spain wins in the category of Throwing Strange Things at each other: La Tomatina. This is where people throw tomatoes at each other. Yes. Really. Tomatoes. No-one really knows why this was started but it has now become extremely popular as over 40,000 people take part every year. By the end of day, the streets are covered in one huge bath of pasta sauce. How fun?

At Anorak, we love carnivals because they remind us that dressing up in amazing costumes is the best fun ever! One of the oldest carnivals ever held is one found in Venice (Italy), where every year since 1162 people make and wear elaborate masks and outfits. The most popular of all carnivals is the one that happens in Rio de Janeiro (Brazil), where over 2 million people take part! Now that's a party!

The festival that wins the most imaginative costumes ever made has to be the Kukeri. Taking place in Bulgaria at the beginning of each year, people dress up as monsters to ward off bad spirits. Some wear gigantic fur-ry heads, others wear masks covered in jewels, thousands of feathers or even flowers. While some may be a little scary, it is all done on purpose: the scarier they are the better they will be at chasing away nasty spirits.

Japan is a country we would easily move Anorak Towers to, and even more so now that we have discovered that they have a day dedicated to celebrating kids and their happiness. Hooray! Held on the 5th day of the 5th month, the Childrens' Festival is a no school day. Double hooray! Children spend the day competing in Kids Olympics and everyone gets to eat mochis (our favourite dessert ever). All houses fly carp-shaped kites outside to remind their children to be as strong as carp, who spend their lives swimming up stream.

HAPPY BIRTHDAY ANORAK!

Thank you to all our lovely friends who took part in our Happy Birthday competition last month. We received some amazingly fun wishes that made us feel all warm inside. How Happy We Are!

Covey (3 years old)

Edith (8 years old)

Maia (7 years old)

Maruko (a few years old)

Jonty (10 years old)

Jimmy (8 years old)

Erica (a few years old)

Theo (6 years old)

Auden (10 years old)

Zoe (a few years old)

Kathryn (a few years old)

Lennie (9 years old)

Dog Knit Sweater (a few years old)

Nommi (6 years old)

Leo (6 years old)

Chloe (11 years old)

Matilde (a few years old)

Celia (a few years old)

Alberta (6 years old)

Emma (a few years old)

SUBSCRIBE TO ANORAK

SUBSCRIBE TO
THE HAPPY MAG FOR KIDS!

Subscribing to Anorak means you get every SINGLE issue delivered to your door by a bunch of teddy bears on rollerskates.*

It also means you get FREE postage. AND you are guaranteed never to miss an issue.

To subscribe, get your Mum, Dad, Gran, Pops or any generous human beings to visit

anorakmagazine.com/shop

Thank you!

C.H

*Please note that we can't always guarantee teddy bears as they often prefer to sleep all day.

SPACE IS FUN!

Words by
Allison Hill
EU UNIVERSE AWARENESS
illustrations by
Pearl Law

There has recently been some happy news from space about the discovery of a new planet. Should we pack our astronaut outfits straight away?

Every time astronomers detect a small, rocky planet in the habitable zone of another star it is cause for excitement as only a handful are known. They have just discovered one called Proxima b. This is an Earth-sized planet orbiting Proxima Centauri, a red dwarf star, and the closest one to our Sun. This is potentially a planet that could have conditions to allow liquid water on the surface. To think it has been in our backyard the entire time!

However, let's not pack our bags just yet! Proxima Centauri might be closer than any other stars, but stars are, in general, very far apart. Travelling at light-speed (which is the fastest speed that you could ever travel), it would still take 4.2 years to reach Proxima b. With current rocket technology, to send humans would take around 100,000 years!

That doesn't mean there is no hope for us visiting Proxima b in our generation. Before the discovery of Proxima b, a group coordinated by cosmologist Stephen Hawking, Facebook's founder Mark Zuckerberg and a billionaire philanthropist called Yuri Milner got together to create 'Project Starshot'.

Project Starshot involves sending a thousand mini-probes, and launching them at Alpha Centauri, the star system with which Proxima Centauri is associated. The project involves pointing a giant laser from Earth directed at these solar sails, which will accelerate the probes to 20% of the speed of light. At this speed, it should only take 20 years to reach Proxima Centauri.

Although a 20-year trip sounds like a long time, it is much more agreeable than 100 000 years. Watch this space!*

*pun intended.

At Anorak, we love the moon. Are there any others in the universe?

Certainly! In fact, there are 173 moons that orbit other planets in our very own solar system.

That doesn't include the moons that orbit dwarf planets, such as Ceres and Pluto. It is even possible to see from Earth the shadows that moons cause on Jupiter using a telescope.

There are billions of stars in our Milky Way galaxy, and billions of galaxies in our universe. Some that we are not even aware of. So it is safe to assume that there are many more moons in the universe than there are stars. We just don't have the technology to see them yet.

**On planet Earth we go round and round.
Do other planets rotate like ours?**

Most of the planets in our solar system rotate just like Earth, but the time it takes to do that on other planets is very different.

The most Earth-like rotator in our solar system is Mars. A day on Mars lasts 24 hours and 40 minutes, which is slightly longer than an Earth day of 24 hours.

From there, the solar system gets a little bit weird.

For example, the length of a day on Jupiter, the largest planet in our solar system, is less than 10 hours!

The longest day in our solar system is on Venus. Venus takes 243 Earth days to rotate once on its axis!

It also rotates in the opposite direction to other planets, so the Sun rises in the West, instead of the East.

How old is our planet? How old are other planets?

The oldest rocks we have ever found on Earth are 4.5 billion years old, which we think is roughly the age of the Solar System.

The Sun and all the planets are thought to have formed at the same time, which makes all the other planets about 4.5 billion years old as well.

Some planets have 'younger' surfaces, such as Venus. It had lots of volcanic activity in its history, which brings to its surface young material from deep within. This means the rocks on the surface of Venus might be younger than those on Earth, but both planets have been around for about the same time.

WEEE!

HAPPY 45600000 000000th BIRTH DAY!

There is nothing more fun than fun itself.
We know because we can't stop having fun.
In case you need a little fun in your life,
this is our guide to having the best fun ever.

JUMPING IN PUDDLES

The most fun way to jump in puddles is to jump in puddles when you've been told not to jump in puddles. That adds at least three gallons of fun to that whole experience. Because it becomes cheeky fun. Cheeky fun is good. We don't reckon you should be shy when jumping in puddles, you should just go for it with utter confidence and gusto. If you don't have boots, don't worry. Jumping in puddles with school shoes or trainers is just as fun. If your parents don't think that's fun, tell them to join in. They'll quickly understand how fun it is.

PAVEMENTS

Pavements are full of surprises. They are, honest. Have you ever tried to step on the lines of a pavement? It can reveal some extraordinary surprises: you might turn into a potato, a pink flamingo, a crocodile might swallow you up or you might wake up some zombies. If you see that happen, contact a grown-up immediately who can give you a 'step on the line' antidote. That's just a potion mostly made of Boredom Dust.

SILLY JOKES

Life can get serious sometimes. When it does, there is only one remedy: silly jokes. They tickle us and make us feel instantly happy. The more the merrier. Want some examples? Here you go:

What do cats eat for breakfast? Mice krispies.

Ahahahahahahahaha. See? Silly but funny.

What kind of food do racehorses eat? Fast food.

Double ahahahahah.

What do the cleverest and funniest kids in the world like to read? Anorak of course.

That's not a joke. That's a true fact.

DANCING

Please practise dancing as much as possible because once you reach the age of 12, you won't want to anymore. It will be seen as embarrassing. Shaking, jumping, pirouetting, it's all fun before the age of 12. Extra fun can be added to dancing by doing it in front of a mirror. That sends us into Dance Land where we are the greatest dancers the world has ever seen. Fact.

How many times can you spot the word 'fun' on these pages?

o   23 ½ times

o   12 million times

o   having too much fun to count.

NATURE iS

Dodo Love

One animal we wish we could have as a pet is the dodo. It would be a little tough as they are now completely extinct. The last one ever was killed in the 15th Century. So not even your granddad could have had one as a pet. While they were classified as birds, they actually couldn't fly. A bit like penguins. The Dodo may have looked like a fancypants turkey, but it used to share most characteristics with the modern day... pigeon!

Hello Heli

Contrary to what its name suggests, the helicoprion is not the ancestor of the helicopter. It is in fact a pretty beastly looking shark that lived many, many years ago. It became extinct over 250 million years ago so don't worry, no risk of swimming into one of them any time soon. The very odd and terrifying thing about it is the row of teeth poking out of its mouth, a bit like a wheel of death. It could grow to 7 metres long, which is roughly 7 of you put together. Charming beast.

Stinky the Stinker

Animals and insects have various ways of protecting themselves: some wear bright red colours, like ladybirds, and others use... a nasty smell! The stinkbug is one of those. When it feels threatened it sprays a foul odour that puts off any potential predators. The stinkbug may be as small as a coin but it has the appetite of an ogre. It has been known to eat bugs much bigger than itself, including caterpillars! An ambitious stinker that one!

FUN!

Pretty in Pink

Armadillos are cute. Pink Fairy Armadillos are even cuter. They don't even need to be actual fairies to be cute. For one, they are pink. Two, they carry around a (pink) shell that works like a radiator, keeping them adequately warm during cold nights. Three, they are teeny tiny delicate creatures, measuring only the same size as your hand. Triple cutie!

Is it a cat? Maybe. A fish? Maybe too. A human? Maybe three.

Cats and fish are natural enemies but in the case of the catfish, Mother Nature has decided to see whether they could co-exist. The catfish doesn't miaow but it has four extraordinary whiskers adorning its extraordinarily big head. One special species found in South East Asia is able to walk! Called the Walking Catfish (original!), it wobbles and slithers around from one water pool to another in search of lunch. Catfish or CatHumanFish?

Ant Hoover

Eating normally means chewing. Not in the case of ant eaters, who don't have any teeth and therefore can't masticate anything. Instead, they hoover up ants by the truckload. They can gobble up as many as 35,000 ants a day, so by truckload we mean truckload! They have a super powerful tongue that looks a little like a worm and can flick up to 160 times in one minute! That's pretty admirable we think, but terrible news if you are an ant.

Words by
Cathy Olmedillas,
illustrations by
Pawel Mildner

ANORAK FUN
BUT EXTREMELY SILLY

JAN 20 – FEB 18

Those born in January are huge fans of socks. That's a fact. This month will see you visiting beaches wearing socks and a blanket, just in case the weather turns.

FEB 19 – MARCH 20

This month you will have pancakes for breakfast, lunch and dinner. You will make sweet pancakes, savoury pancakes and even both sweet and savoury pancakes.

MAR 21 – APR 19

Careful with sniffing too many flowers as it will induce a lot of sneezing and your nose might fly off. If it does fly off, call a doctor.

APR 20 – MAY 20

Pretending that your dog chewed your homework will get you in trouble with Mrs LaBadTeacher so it will be easier if you behave and do your revision after all.

MAY 21 – JUN 20

You will have an uncontrollable urge to dance wildly from the moment you wake up tomorrow and for the whole month ahead. Do not resist and instead enjoy a month of jigging. It is good for your fitness.

JUN 21 – JUL 22

You might make two very good friends on the way to school. Then again you might not. It all depends if you wake up in a friendly mood.

HOROSCOPES

JUL 23 – AUG 22

Today will be a great day as you will learn how to dance backwards. You may even receive a letter of congratulations from the Queen of Backwards Dancing, Lady Bee.

AUG 23 – SEPT 22

Do not leave your bed for a whole month; that's the only reasonable advice we can give you as two of your planets are in sleeping mode and one must always follow our planets' example.

SEPT 23 – OCT 22

It may be a good month, or it may be a bad month for you: all you need to do is decide. If you decide it will be good, then it will be good.

OCT 23 – NOV 21

If you have been praying to receive a visit from aliens, your prayers might be answered this month. They will come unannounced so stay alert.

NOV 22 – DEC 21

You might feel a little tired this month but don't worry, it's only a phase. Next month, you will spend it sleeping so you won't feel tired at all.

DEC 22 – JAN 19

You will spot a spider and if you stroke it, it will bring you good luck for the rest of your life.

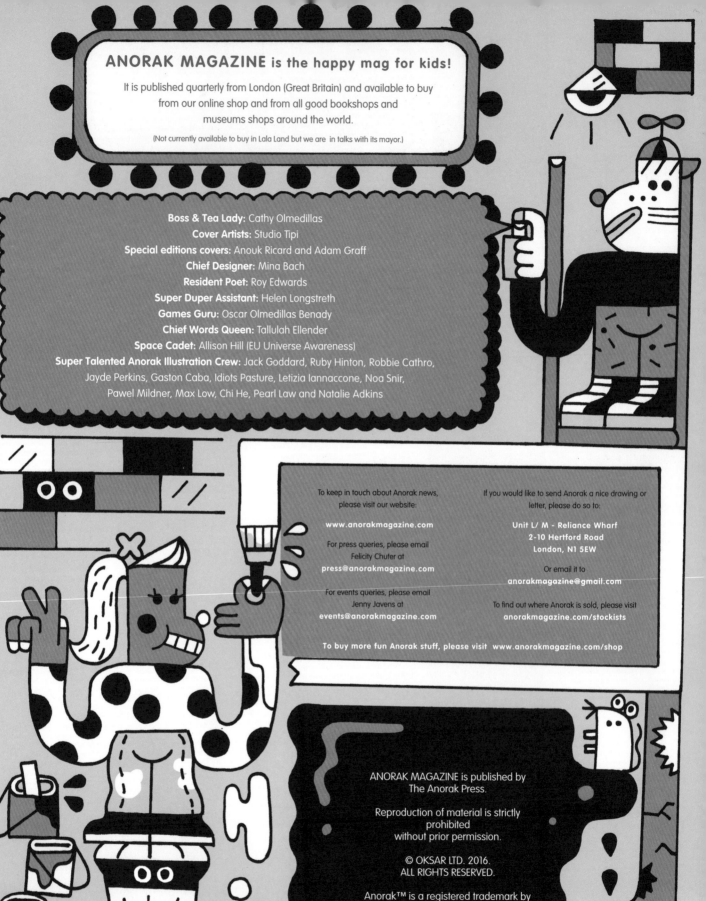

ANORAK MAGAZINE is the happy mag for kids!

It is published quarterly from London (Great Britain) and available to buy from our online shop and from all good bookshops and museums shops around the world.

(Not currently available to buy in Lala Land but we are in talks with its mayor.)

Boss & Tea Lady: Cathy Olmedillas
Cover Artists: Studio Tipi
Special editions covers: Anouk Ricard and Adam Graff
Chief Designer: Mina Bach
Resident Poet: Roy Edwards
Super Duper Assistant: Helen Longstreth
Games Guru: Oscar Olmedillas Benady
Chief Words Queen: Tallulah Ellender
Space Cadet: Allison Hill (EU Universe Awareness)
Super Talented Anorak Illustration Crew: Jack Goddard, Ruby Hinton, Robbie Cathro, Jayde Perkins, Gaston Caba, Idiots Pasture, Letizia Iannaccone, Noa Snir, Pawel Mildner, Max Low, Chi He, Pearl Law and Natalie Adkins

To keep in touch about Anorak news, please visit our website:

www.anorakmagazine.com

For press queries, please email Felicity Chuter at
press@anorakmagazine.com

For events queries, please email Jenny Javens at
events@anorakmagazine.com

To buy more fun Anorak stuff, please visit www.anorakmagazine.com/shop

If you would like to send Anorak a nice drawing or letter, please do so to:

Unit L/ M - Reliance Wharf
2-10 Hertford Road
London, N1 5EW

Or email it to
anorakmagazine@gmail.com

To find out where Anorak is sold, please visit
anorakmagazine.com/stockists